To Jessica —

May God bless you!

—Kimberly [illegible]

Grandma Had a Grandma Too by Kimberly Luttery

Published by
Azure Dusk Publishing, LLC

Cover design and illustrations by Nicole Collie

Azure Dusk Publishing, LLC
P.O. Box 1122
Conley, GA 30288

Web address: www.kimberlyluttery.com

Library of Congress Control Number: 2016909738
ISBN 978-0-9797172-0-8
Audience: 3 & Up
10 9 8 7 6 5 4 3 2 1
1. Children 2. Picture Book 3. Easy Readers
First Printing

Printed in the United States of America

For Mom - My forever angel and biggest cheerleader.

Mya – My little inspiration.

To my best friend and husband Ray, thank you for your love, your support, and for pushing me further.

Kimberly

Grandma Had a Grandma Too

Nia loves playing with her grandmother Nana, but has a hard time imagining that Nana was ever a child. **Grandma Had a Grandma Too** takes the reader on a journey back in time with a young Nana and her own grandmother...fishing at the creek, chasing fireflies at dusk, eating blackberries from the backyard and more. This story affirms that the simplest times we share with a child can create the most beloved and cherished memories.

Grandma Had a Grandma Too appeals to children ages 3 - 8 years old, but older children and adults will love it as well. The simplicity of the language is perfect for reading aloud as a bedtime or anytime story.

One day I asked my grandma
Exactly how old are you?
I really want to know Nana
Are you ninety or ninety-two?

Grandma laughed out loud,
And then smiled
Oh Nia, I wasn't born this way
I was once a little child
Back then I had no gray

I also had a grandma
When I was young like you
Yes, Grandma had a grandma
And she loved me as I love you

What did you do with your grandma?
Nana, I really want to know

Did you blow wishes with dandelions
Or make angels in the snow?

We sat on her front porch
While sipping homemade tea
Rocking in big rocking chairs
Enjoying the summer breeze

Sometimes we lounged in the grass
Under weeping willow trees
She'd lay a blanket on the ground
And we snapped fresh sugar peas

We often danced in the sun
While the wind whipped through our hair
Through the grass we'd jump and run
The smell of roses filled the air

Picking berries wet with morning dew
Our fingers got sticky and sweet
We ate them 'til our tongues turned blue
From the plump and juicy treat

Wow! Tell me more Nana
'Cause that sounds like so much fun
I bet they tasted really good
Now I wish that I had some

We chased dragonflies at the creek
And slid worms on fishing hooks

Water rippled through our feet
As we caught fish by the brook

I climbed her great big maple tree
And spotted the first twinkling star

We made angel wings from leaves
And caught lightning bugs with a jar

In the evening I helped her bake
Licking batter from the spoon
We ate scrumptious lemon pound cake
While we spied the glowing moon

I bet she sang sweet lullabies
As she tucked you in at night
And before you closed your sleepy eyes
Did your grandma hug you tight?

Yes, she sang sweet melodies
While I snuck a final peek

Then I'd have the sweetest dreams
After I kissed her on the cheek

She made those days so much fun
With her kind and easy way
I couldn't wait for more to come
And I miss her every day

I like to keep her picture near
To see her lovely smile
It almost feels as if she's here
If only for a while

Every time that I'm with you
Reminds me of those days
One day you'll have a grandchild too
And think of me this way

So you see Nia, I also had a grandma
When I was young like you
Yes, Grandma had a grandma
And she loved me as I love you

You're the best grandma, Nana
But, I have one more thing to say
I know you loved your grandma
And I love you the very same way

 Have an adult help you fill in family names, birth dates, and birth city/state.

Grandma's name is ___________________________

Grandma's birth date and year born ___________________________

My grandma was born in (city, state) ___________________________

What was her grandma's name? ___________________________

Grandma's favorite color is ___________________________

Grandma's favorite song is ___________________________

Grandma's favorite hobby is ___________________________

Grandma's favorite food is ___________________________

What I love most about my grandma is ___________________________

My favorite thing to do with grandma is ___________________________

Grandma has (how many) ____ brothers____ and/or _____ sisters

Grandma has (how many) ____ grandchildren

What else would you like to write about grandma? _______________

____

fun facts about My Grandma

About the Author

Kimberly Luttery's passion for creative writing began at a very young age with short stories and poetry. After receiving a B.A. degree in Mass Communications from Illinois State University, she spent much of her career working with non-profit organizations that focus on family and children.

"I am passionate about **Grandma Had a Grandma Too** because it is inspired by the real life relationship between my mother and niece. They share such a fun and loving friendship and I wanted to capture it in words. What started out as a personal poem soon grew into the vision for this story--a beautifully illustrated picture book."

This is Kimberly's debut picture book, and the first in a series of stories for children about life and love with universal appeal. Kimberly resides in suburban Atlanta with her husband Ray. You can find out more about her work at **www.KimberlyLuttery.com.**

About the Illustrator

Nicole Collie's love affair with art began at an early age with paintings of landscapes and flowers, and later, human beings. Acrylics is her favorite medium, and she constantly experiments with new ways to put color on canvas. Much of her art is inspired by her desire for people to love themselves. For Nicole, color is a language and as an artist, she is the interpreter.

Nicole received a degree in Graphic Design from the Art Institute of Pittsburgh and has shown her work for the last 12 years at galleries in her native Bahamas, as well as Atlanta, Los Angeles, Memphis, and more.

Nicole says, "What I sincerely love about this book is that it means as much to the parent reading the story as it does to the child being read to. I have fond memories of my own relationship with my grandmother and am able to share some of those memories with my son. It is very touching." Visit **www.NicoleCollie.com** to see more of her work.